D0717931
£2.65

Quick now! Put your name down here!
This Book belongs to

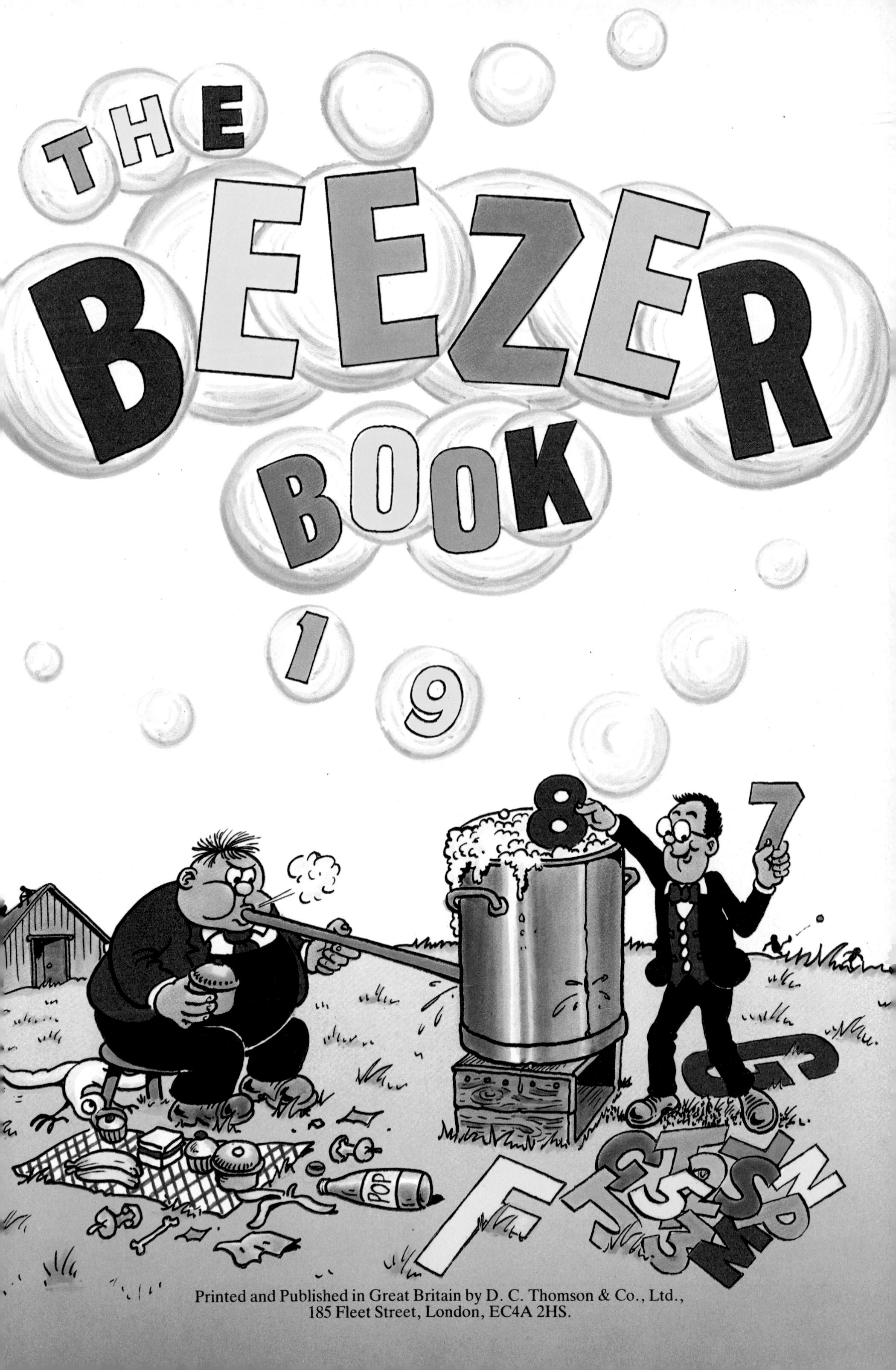

Printed and Published in Great Britain by D. C. Thomson & Co., Ltd.,
185 Fleet Street, London, EC4A 2HS.

A bit of a lark with a bench in the park!

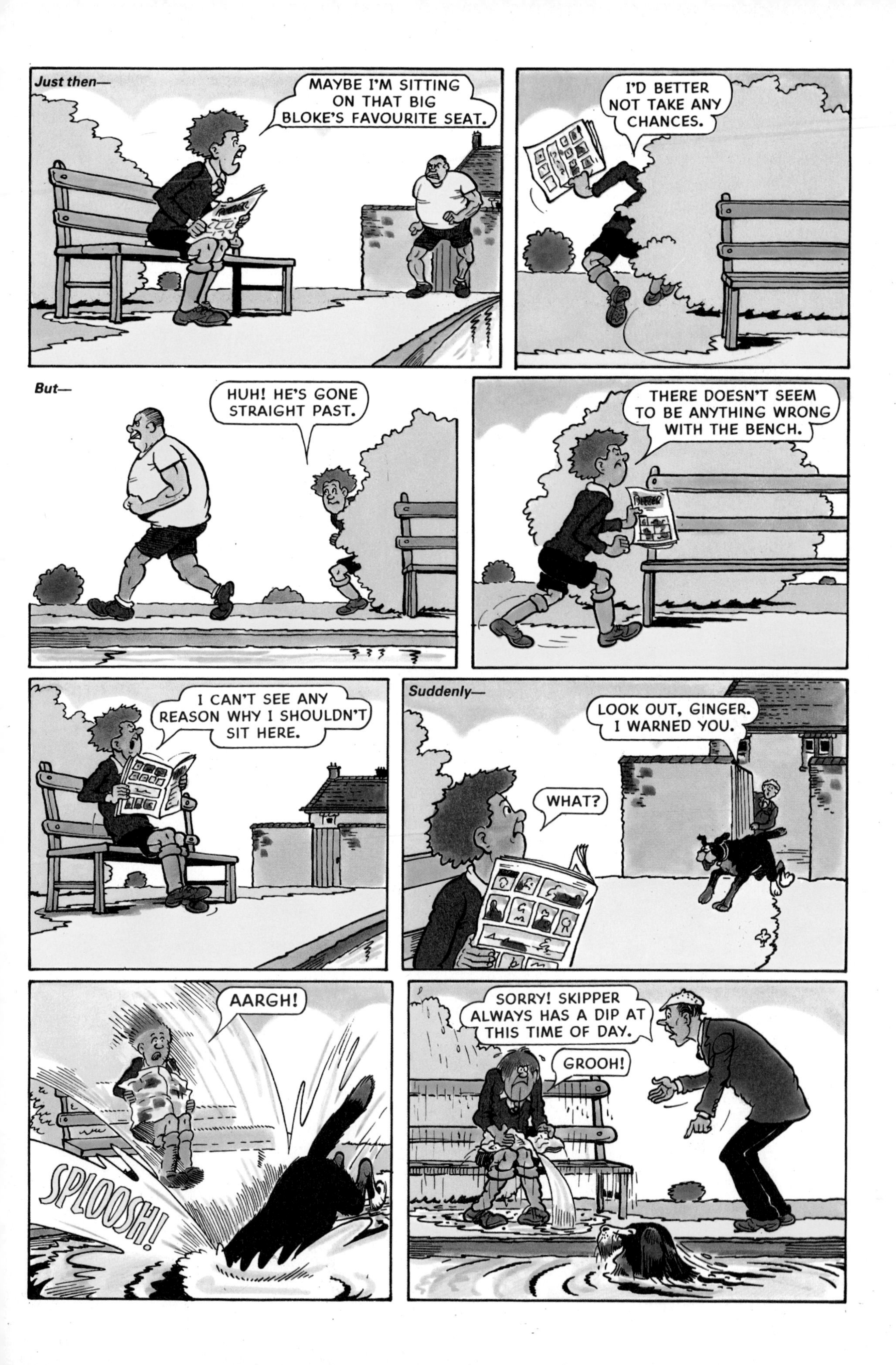

Just then—
MAYBE I'M SITTING ON THAT BIG BLOKE'S FAVOURITE SEAT.
I'D BETTER NOT TAKE ANY CHANCES.
But—
HUH! HE'S GONE STRAIGHT PAST.
THERE DOESN'T SEEM TO BE ANYTHING WRONG WITH THE BENCH.
I CAN'T SEE ANY REASON WHY I SHOULDN'T SIT HERE.
Suddenly—
LOOK OUT, GINGER. I WARNED YOU.
WHAT?
AARGH!
SPLOOSH!
SORRY! SKIPPER ALWAYS HAS A DIP AT THIS TIME OF DAY.
GROOH!

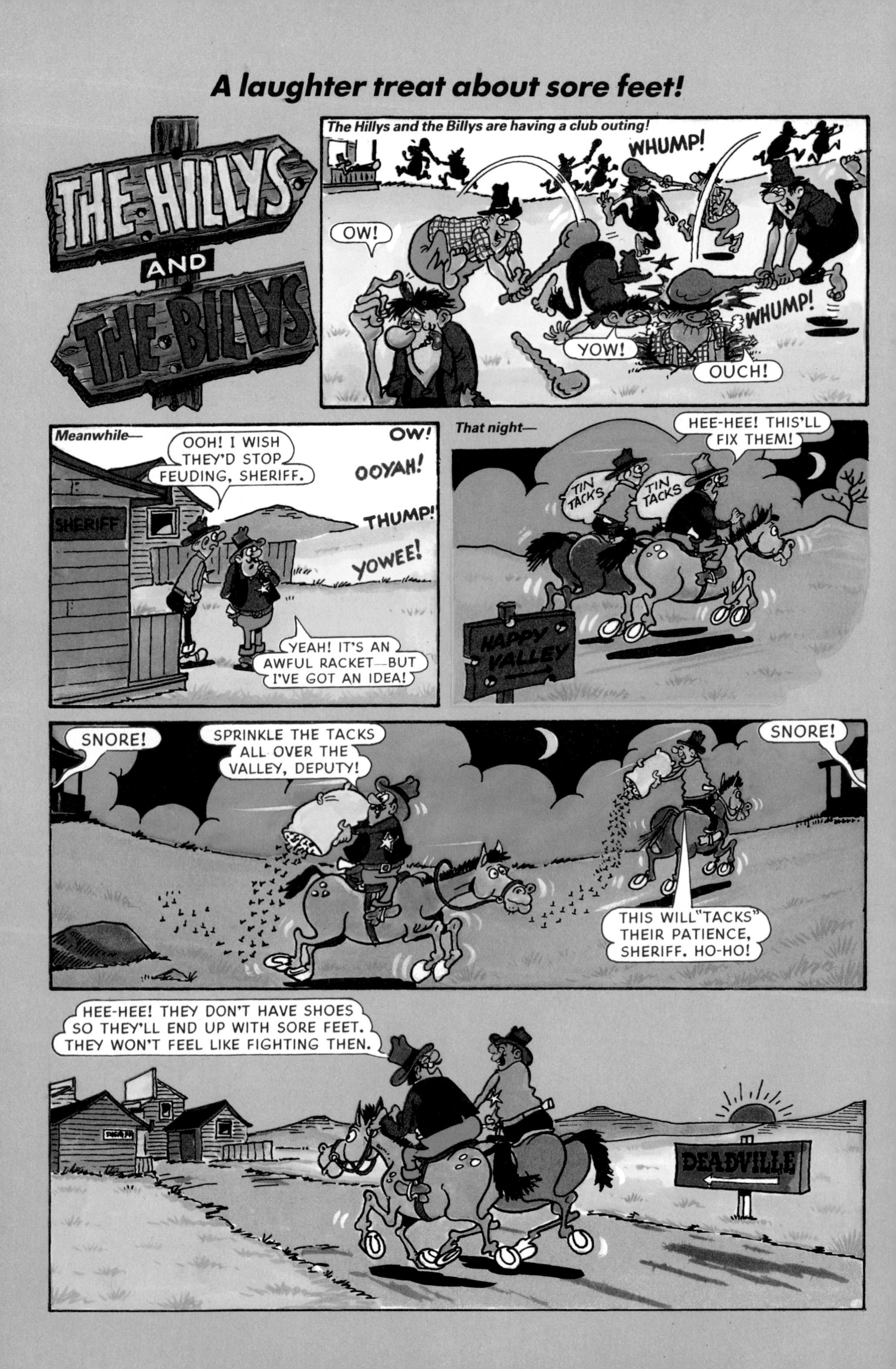
A laughter treat about sore feet!
THE HILLYS AND THE BILLYS
The Hillys and the Billys are having a club outing!
WHUMP!
OW!
YOW!
WHUMP!
OUCH!
Meanwhile—
OOH! I WISH THEY'D STOP FEUDING, SHERIFF.
SHERIFF
OW!
OOYAH!
THUMP!
YOWEE!
YEAH! IT'S AN AWFUL RACKET—BUT I'VE GOT AN IDEA!
That night—
HEE-HEE! THIS'LL FIX THEM!
TIN TACKS
TIN TACKS
HAPPY VALLEY
SNORE!
SPRINKLE THE TACKS ALL OVER THE VALLEY, DEPUTY!
SNORE!
THIS WILL "TACKS" THEIR PATIENCE, SHERIFF. HO-HO!
HEE-HEE! THEY DON'T HAVE SHOES SO THEY'LL END UP WITH SORE FEET. THEY WON'T FEEL LIKE FIGHTING THEN.
DEADVILLE

Next morning—
YIPPEEE! BILLY-BASHING TIME AGAIN.
COME ON, BILLYS! LET'S CLOBBER THEM HILLYS!
Suddenly—
YEEOUCH!
YEE-OW!
AAIEE!
OW!
Later—
WE CAN'T FEUD WITH THESE FEET, BUT WE CAN GET RID OF THE TACKS!
Some time later—
OOPS! WHAT WAS THAT?
BANG!
BANG!
BANG!
BAH! FLAT TYRES! I'LL HAVE TO WALK INTO TOWN AND GET HELP!
LOOK AFTER MY TRUCK,WILL YOU?
OKAY!
HEY! LOOK WHAT'S ON THE TRUCK.
YIPPEE! OUR PROBLEMS ARE SOLVED!

In town—
IS THERE A GARAGE AROUND HERE? MY LORRY-LOAD OF SCOOTERS IS STUCK IN HAPPY VALLEY!
SHERIFF
I HOPE YOU LEFT A GUARD!
OF COURSE! TWO OLD GEEZERS WITH BANDAGED FEET ARE GUARDING THE SCOOTERS!
OH, NO!
FOLLOW ME, DEPUTY! QUICK!
I RECKON WE'RE TOO LATE, SHERIFF!
BAH! THEY'RE FEUDING AGAIN AND THE NOISE IS WORSE THAN EVER!
VROOM!
BRROOOMM!
CRASH!
HELP!
BAM!
PUFF-PUFF!
BRRM!
TAKE THAT!
PUTT!
EEK!
ZONK!
BRRM!

Staying in bed means trouble ahead!

WELL, DON'T STAY THERE ALL DAY. IT'S NOT GOOD FOR YOU!
In the cupboard—
HM! I WONDER IF I CAN BREAK DOWN THE DOOR WITH THIS.
HERE GOES.
THUMP!
Then—
OOH! MY HEAD! IT'S THUMPING!
THUMP! THUMP!
OOH!
HOWL!
EEK!
OUCH!
OOYAH!

THUMP!
GRR! WE'LL MAKE BRAINY STOP THAT.
THUMP!
WE'LL TEACH HIM NOT TO MAKE A NOISE.
Suddenly—
PHEW! FREE AT LAST! OOPS!
AAGH!
EEK!
OW!
IT SERVES THEM RIGHT. NOW I'LL TELL OUR MAN TO GO OUT INTO THE GARDEN!
MOAN!
BRAIN DEPT.
GO INTO THE GARDEN
SUGGESTION BOX
GROAN!
And—
I'VE GOT A BIT OF A HEADACHE. MAYBE A SPELL IN THE GARDEN WILL HELP!
Soon after—
I THOUGHT YOU WERE STAYING IN BED?
I HAD A BIT OF A HEADACHE. BUT IT'S GONE NOW!
HO-HO! THEY'VE ALL GOT HEADACHES INSTEAD!

A super hoot with hidden loot!

TWIT! IS AN OLD ACCORDION ALL YOU COULD FIND?
WELL, IT WAS DARK IN THERE, BOSS.
WAIL!
Just then—
HOI! MY ACCORDION! COME BACK WITH IT!
RUN! IT'S NOT WORTH GETTING NICKED FOR THIS OLD THING!
Back at the hideout—
NOW THAT WE HAVE IT, WE MIGHT AS WELL PUT IT TO GOOD USE! LET'S ROB A JEWELLER'S WITH IT!
EH?
Early next morning—
JEWELLERS
WATCHES CLOCKS
I'LL PLAY THIS SO BADLY, THE JEWELLER WILL COME OUT TO COMPLAIN, AND WHILE HE'S OUT, YOU NIP IN AND GRAB SOME JEWELLERY.
READY, LADS?
SCREECH
YEOWL!
GROAN!
STOP THAT AWFUL DIN!
HMM! I'LL HAVE TO FIX HER BEFORE THE PLAN CAN WORK.
GLUB!
SPLOOSH!
HAVE THESE EAR-MUFFS, MADAM. THEN YOU WON'T HEAR MY PLAYING.

YEOWL!
SCREECH!
WAIL!
THIS TIME!
GROAN!
In the jeweller's back shop—
IS THE NOISE ANNOYING YOU TOO, ROVER?
SCREECH!
GROAN!
WAIL!
YELP!
THEN DO SOMETHING ABOUT IT!
GROWL!
YERK!
GROAN!
WAIL!
RIP!
THAT MUST BE THE CASH THAT MAJOR DAY REPORTED STOLEN!
WHAT?
One arrest later—
SLAM!
GRR! YOU HEARD THE POLICE ADVISING PEOPLE TO HIDE THEIR VALUABLES IN UNUSUAL PLACES! WHY DIDN'T YOU LOOK IN THE ACCORDION?
SIGH! I GET THE BLAME AS USUAL!

Holiday fun with the short-sighted one!

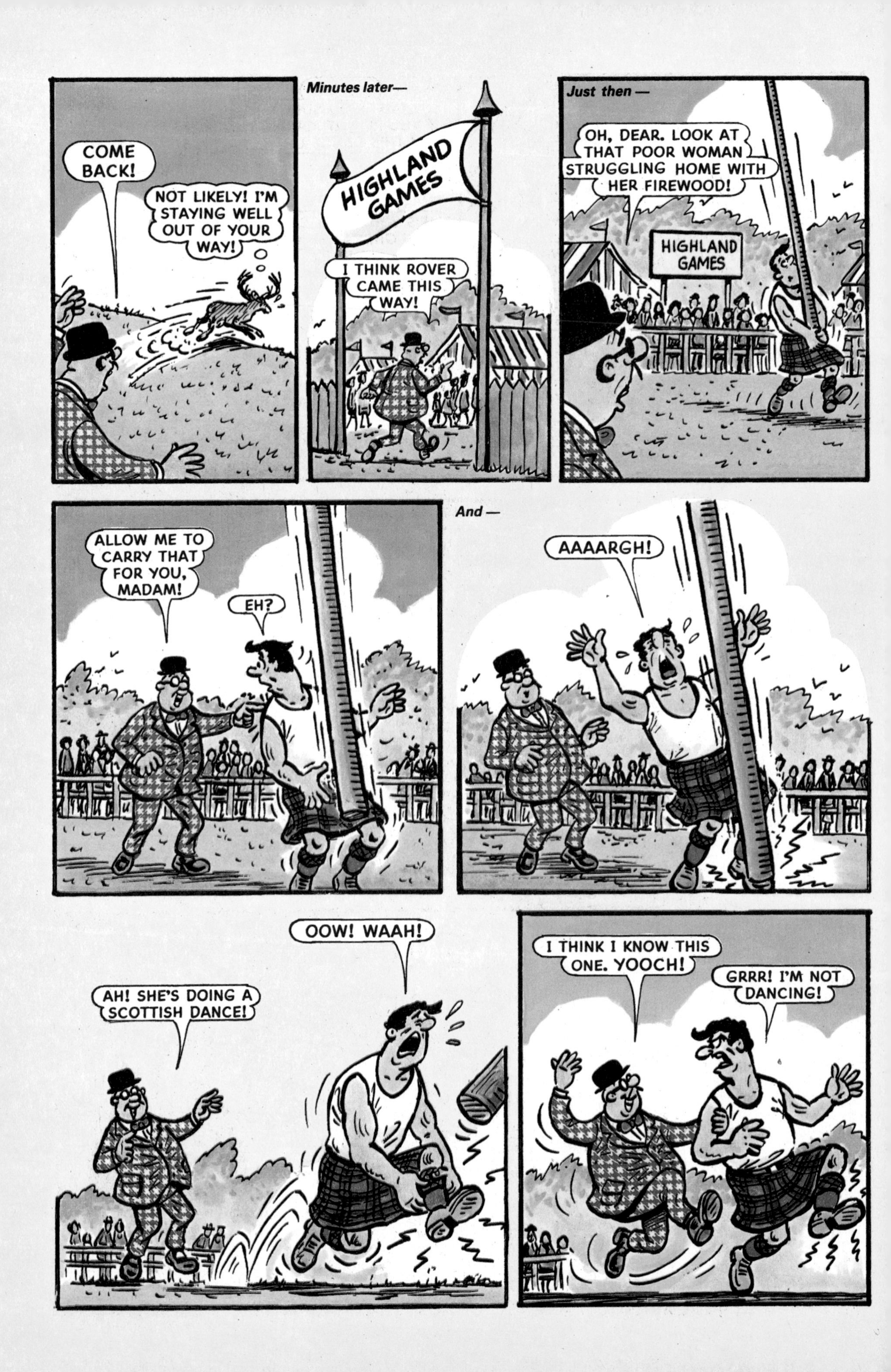
COME BACK!
NOT LIKELY! I'M STAYING WELL OUT OF YOUR WAY!
Minutes later—
HIGHLAND GAMES
I THINK ROVER CAME THIS WAY!
Just then —
OH, DEAR. LOOK AT THAT POOR WOMAN STRUGGLING HOME WITH HER FIREWOOD!
HIGHLAND GAMES
ALLOW ME TO CARRY THAT FOR YOU, MADAM!
EH?
And —
AAAARGH!
AH! SHE'S DOING A SCOTTISH DANCE!
OOW! WAAH!
I THINK I KNOW THIS ONE. YOOCH!
GRRR! I'M NOT DANCING!

I'LL FIX YOU!
WAIT A MINUTE! I'VE NEVER DANCED THESE STEPS!
WAAH! ARE YOU SURE YOU'RE NOT MAKING THIS DANCE UP?
IT'S WHAT YOU CALL A HIGHLAND FLING! HO-HO!
BAH! PESKY TOURIST!
HELP! WHERE AM I?
Meanwhile, at Cousin Angus's —
WHAT DO YOU THINK OF MY HUNTING TROPHIES, AUNTIE?
THEY'RE WONDERFUL! PITY BLINKY WASN'T HERE TO SEE THEM!
Suddenly —
CRACK!
CRASH!
RUMBLE!
ER . . . HELLO, FOLKS! SORRY TO POP IN LIKE THIS!
ACH, BLINKY! YOU'VE JUST REMINDED ME. I FORGOT TO GIVE YOU A FRONT DOOR KEY.

Puzzle

1. In days gone by, the vikings roamed the seas in vessels like this and struck terror into their foes. Do you know what their ships were called? Were they:-
(a) Galleons? (b) Coracles?
(c) Longships?

3. This plant grows in rough grassland in Britain. The hooks on the flower are used to comb out loose material on newly-woven cloth in the woollen industry. Is it a:— (a) Teasel? (b) Thistle? (c) Liverwort?

5. Stoats feed on small rodents such as mice and voles. In winter, their coats change colour from brown to white. A stoat's winter coat has a special name. Is it:—
(a) Mink? (b) Coney?
(c) Ermine?

7. In the days of Robin Hood, archers had longbows made from the tree whose leaves and berries are shown in the foreground. It was used because the wood is very strong and springy. Do you know the name of the tree? Is it :— (a) Yew? (b) Oak? (c) Elm?

2. This butterfly is common all over Britain in the summer and although we steer clear of nettles, it actually lays its eggs on them. Then, when the caterpillars hatch, they eat the nettle leaves. Is it a:— (a) Cabbage White? (b) Painted Lady? (c) Red Admiral?

4. You can see swans on many British lakes and rivers, but be very careful when you're near one. An angry swan will attack anything or anyone who threatens its youngsters. Do you know the correct name for the young swans? Are they:—(a) Leverets? (b) Cygnets? (c) Goslings?

ANSWERS

1-(c). 2-(c). 3-(a).
4-(b). 5-(c). 6-(a).
7-(a). 8-(b).

6. Cars similar to the one above were the first ever to be mass-produced in America. If you're lucky, you may see one in a vintage car rally or museum. Is it a:—(a) Model T Ford? (b) Morris Minor? (c) Jaguar?

8. Opened to the public in 1965, this building has become one of London's best-known landmarks. It is 619 feet tall and is situated in Maple Street, near Piccadilly Circus. Is it:— (a) Cleopatra's Needle? (b) The Post Office Tower? (c) The Planetarium?

When it comes to eatin' — Hoss can't be beaten!

I'LL SNEAK UP AND GRAB SOME OF THAT GRUB.
TRIP
OOPS!
CLASH
CLANG
SOMEBODY'S TRIPPED OVER OUR ALARM.
MAYBE IT'S THE POSSE.
BAH! IT'S ONLY HOSS. DON'T DO THAT AGAIN, YOU DUMMY.
Soon after—
I'LL PRETEND TO BE AN INDIAN AND SCARE THEM OFF.
GO AWAY, HOSS. WE ALL KNOW INJUNS NEVER FIGHT IN THE DARK.

I MUST SIT DOWN AND THINK. HOW CAN I GET SOME OF THAT GRUB?
Then—
OOOO
OOWW
CAN YOUR HORSE HOWL?
HORSES CAN'T HOWL! ONLY WOLVES HOWL!
WOLVES? LET'S GET OUT OF HERE!
HEY, GUYS! WAIT FOR ME!
WHO SAYS HORSES CAN'T HOWL? WHEN THEY'RE HURT ENOUGH AND HUNGRY ENOUGH, THEY'LL HOWL! MUNCH! MUNCH!

Mum's slick, Wild West trick!

HELP! SOMEBODY TURN OFF THE WATER SUPPLY!
Outside—
IT'S A LOVELY DAY TO HANG OUT WASHING!
Suddenly—
THUD
OUCH!
WAAH!
SMIFFY! SO YOU'RE TRYING TO ESCAPE WITHOUT HAVING A BATH, ARE YOU? WE'LL SEE ABOUT THAT!
OH, NO! JUST MY LUCK TO LAND ON MUM.
COME BACK HERE!
NOT LIKELY!
FAIRGROUND
ALL RIGHT THEN. HAVE IT YOUR OWN WAY!

GOTCHA!
HOOK A DUCK
SKID
AARGH!
WATCHING THOSE COWBOY FILMS HAS FINALLY PAID OFF. HO-HO!
COME ON, SMIFFY. OUT YOU COME!
WHEN WE GET HOME, I'M GOING TO MAKE SURE YOU HAVE A BATH.
BUT I'M SOAKING ALREADY, MUM.
And then—
HELP! TURN OFF THE WATER!
OH, NO!
AH, WELL, I CAN'T HAVE A BATH AFTER ALL. DAD'S USING THE WATER! HO-HO!

Sue's sweet treat!

SORRY! I CAN'T STOP!
HOI! MY PAPER!
Then—
EEK! MY KNITTING! WHAT ARE YOU DOING, SUE?
SORRY! I CAN'T STOP TO EXPLAIN!
AND NOW, THE GOLDFISH BOWL!
But then—
HEY!
OOPS! I'VE HIT DAD'S PILE OF BOOKS!
SORRY! I CAN'T STOP RIGHT NOW!
I'LL GET AN AWFUL ROW WHEN I GET HOME, BUT I THINK THE PRACTICE WAS WORTH IT!
SWEET SHOP
And—
THAT LETTER SAID I'D WON A COMPETITION, AND THIS IS MY PRIZE—AS MANY SWEETS AS I CAN GATHER IN TWO MINUTES!
PAY HERE
PICK-N-MIX
CHOC

It's a piece of cake catching crooks with a brake!

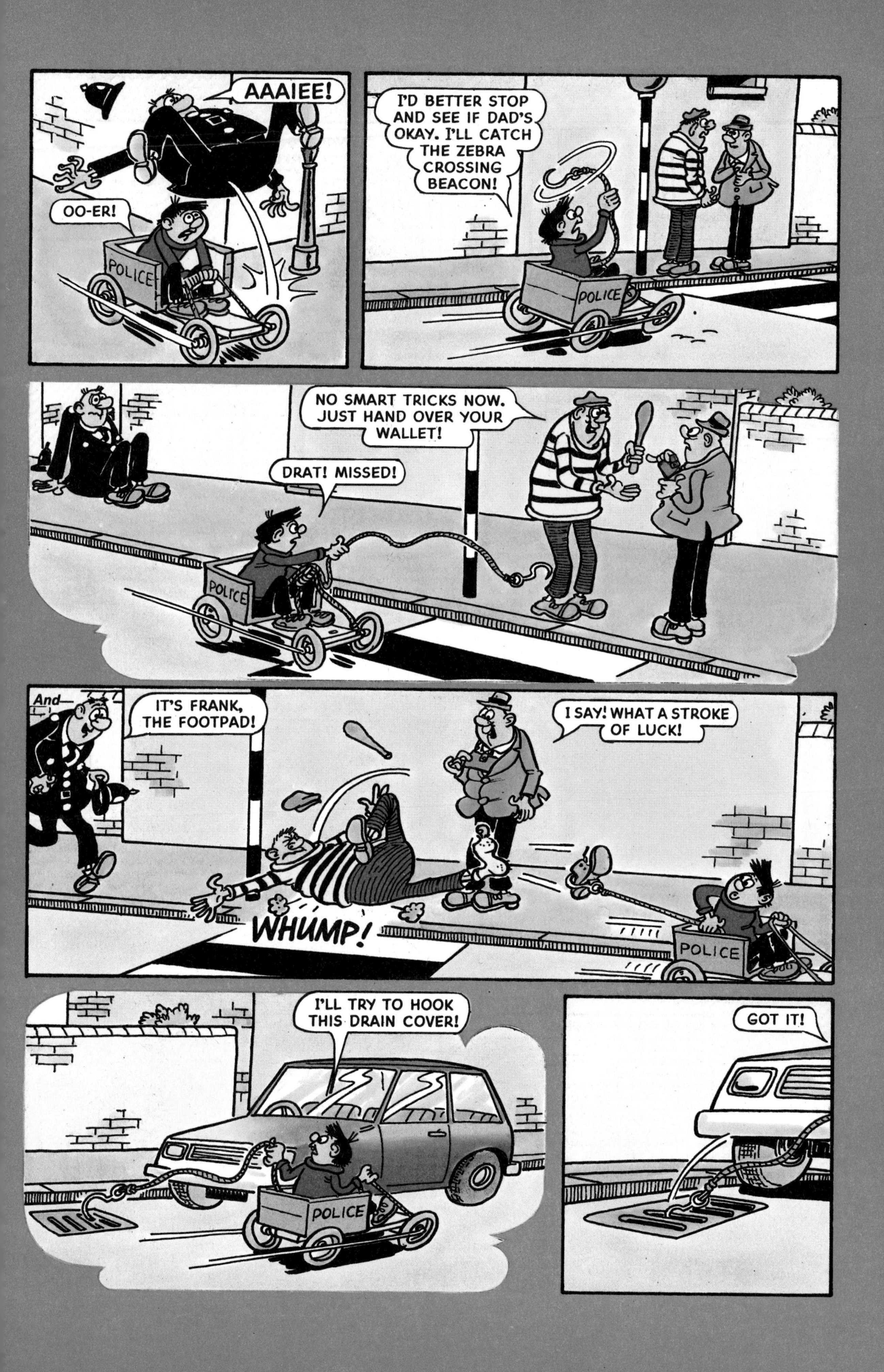
AAAIEE!
OO-ER!
I'D BETTER STOP AND SEE IF DAD'S OKAY. I'LL CATCH THE ZEBRA CROSSING BEACON!
NO SMART TRICKS NOW. JUST HAND OVER YOUR WALLET!
DRAT! MISSED!
And—
IT'S FRANK, THE FOOTPAD!
I SAY! WHAT A STROKE OF LUCK!
WHUMP!
I'LL TRY TO HOOK THIS DRAIN COVER!
GOT IT!

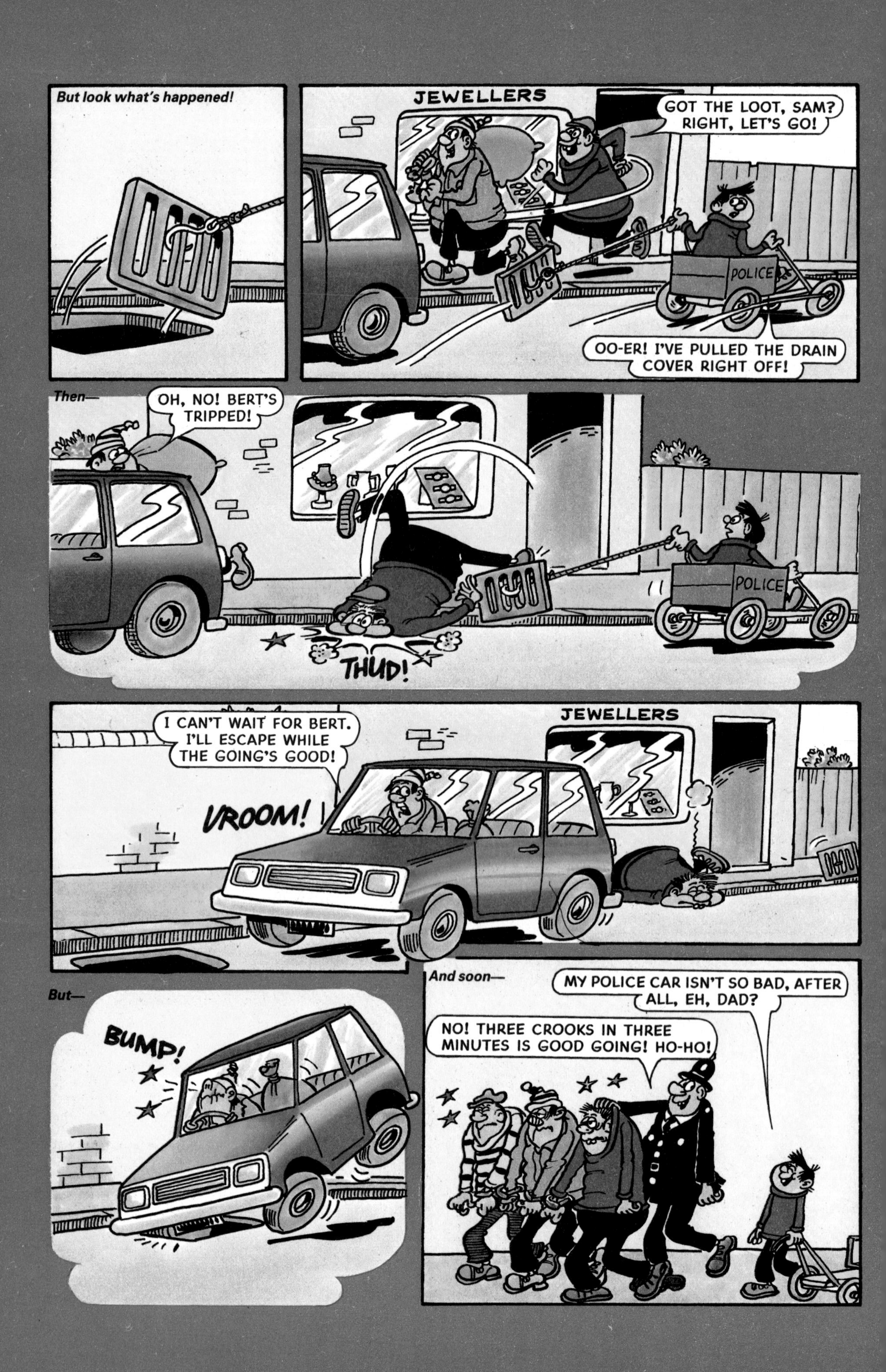

But look what's happened!
JEWELLERS
GOT THE LOOT, SAM? RIGHT, LET'S GO!
POLICE
OO-ER! I'VE PULLED THE DRAIN COVER RIGHT OFF!
Then—
OH, NO! BERT'S TRIPPED!
POLICE
THUD!
JEWELLERS
I CAN'T WAIT FOR BERT. I'LL ESCAPE WHILE THE GOING'S GOOD!
VROOM!
But—
BUMP!
And soon—
MY POLICE CAR ISN'T SO BAD, AFTER ALL, EH, DAD?
NO! THREE CROOKS IN THREE MINUTES IS GOOD GOING! HO-HO!

The Bunch are in danger from a hairy stranger!

OH, NO! THE POINT'S BROKEN OFF MY PENCIL.
COME ON, FATTY. YOU CAN TELL US LATER.
GOR
BUT IT'S IMPORTANT. THERE WAS A MESSAGE ON THE RADIO.
AH! NOW I UNDERSTAND. YOU WANT TO BRING YOUR RADIO.
NO, YOU IDIOT! LOOK! I'M TRYING TO WARN YOU ABOUT A GORILLA.
COME ON, YOU BIG APE!
Soon after—
YUMMY! THOSE BOYS ARE EATING BANANAS!
HAND THEM OVER! I'M STARVING!
AAAAARGH!
I HAVEN'T HAD A BITE TO EAT SINCE I ESCAPED FROM THE ZOO.
HEY! MAYBE THAT FAT ONE HAS BANANAS, TOO!
HELP! IT'S GLADYS!

COME BACK HERE!
MMPH!
SLIP!
OUCH!
LOOK, SID. THAT YOUNG LAD'S FLATTENED GLADYS.
ZOO
WELL DONE, SON!
HERE'S SOME BANANAS FOR YOUR TROUBLE.
ZOO
COO! THANKS!
HI, BOYS! IF YOU HADN'T CLAMPED MY JAWS SHUT I COULD'VE WARNED YOU ABOUT THAT GORILLA. ANYONE FANCY A CAKE?
ER . . . NO THANKS! I'VE GONE OFF THE IDEA OF HAVING A PICNIC.

What a scream with whipped cream!

CAN'T YOU DO ANYTHING RIGHT? TRY MAKING CREAM HORNS. THAT WAY THE CREAM WON'T SQUIRT OUT SO EASILY!
So—
KRAK!
THIS CREAM HORN IS BRICK HARD!
WAK!
NO PROBLEM, SIR. I'LL SHOW YOU HOW TO GET THE CREAM OUT.
ZZZZT!
A-A-A-A-
FLOT!
AAAGGG!
THAT FAT OAF SQUIRTED CREAM ALL OVER ME!
I KNOW HOW TO DEAL WITH HIM. FIRST, WE ROLL UP THIS PIECE OF PAPER, LIKE SO.

THEN WE FILL IT WITH CREAM.
SCHLOP!
CALL THAT A CREAM HORN? IT'S TOO BIG, AND IT'S MADE OF PAPER. IT'S NO USE!
YOU'RE WRONG! IT'S PERFECT!
SPLUD!
HO-HO! THAT HORN SUITS YOU, DAN! IT LOOKS LIKE A DUNCE'S CAP!

OUR SHERIFF'S AN APE!

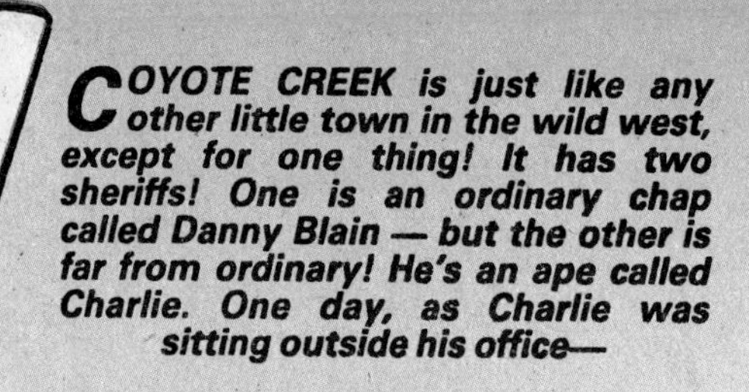

SHERIFF'S OFFICE

LET'S BUY A SET OF SKITTLES, HANK!

GOOD IDEA, CHUCK!

So—
JUST TRY TO KNOCK THE SKITTLES OVER WITH THE BALL.
Whee! The big ape threw the ball at the skittles with all his might — and missed completely!
WOW!
EEK!
A poor cowboy suddenly got an awful headache . . .
OOYAH!
HOTEL
. . . and an unexpected bath!

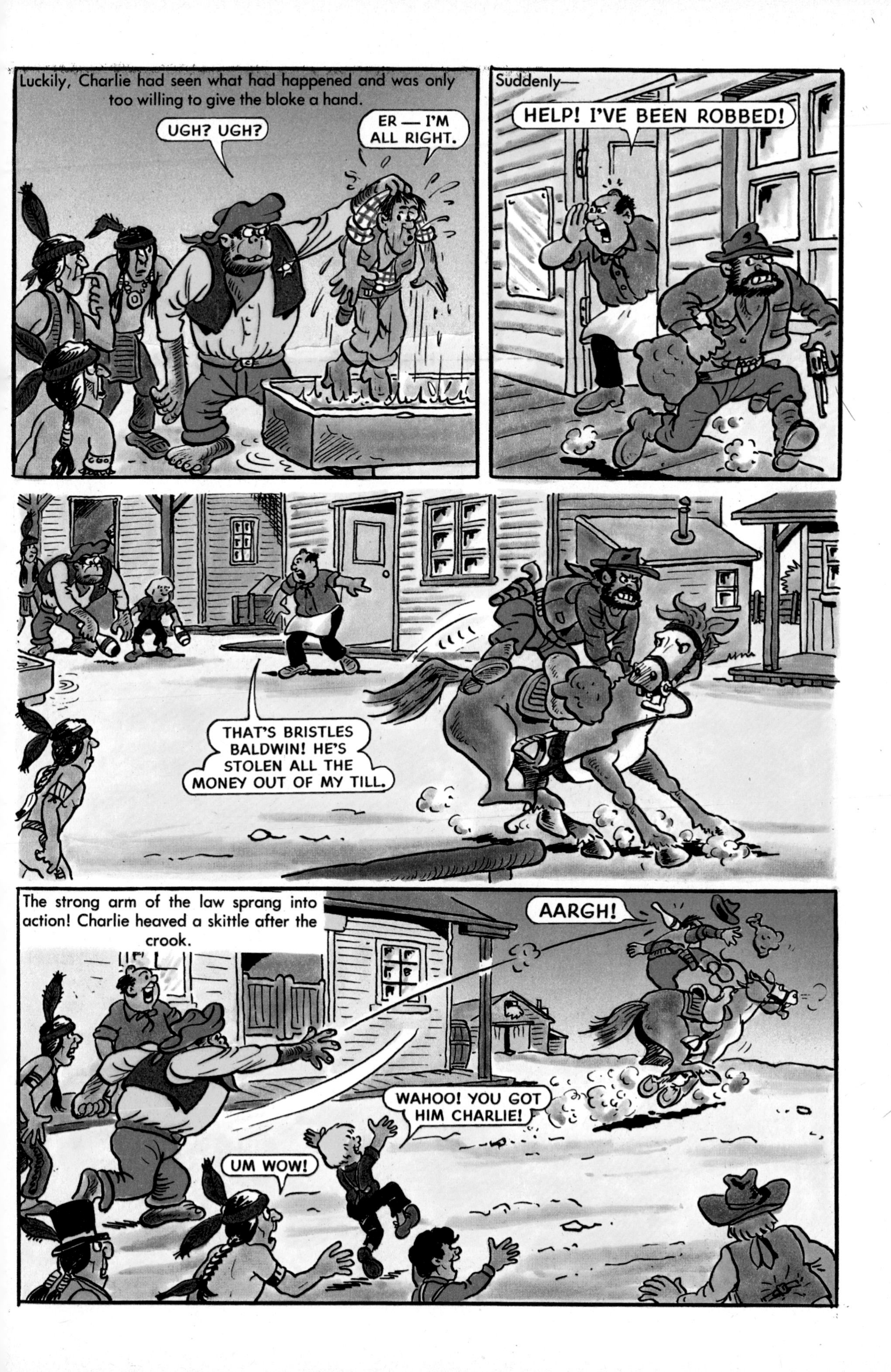
Luckily, Charlie had seen what had happened and was only too willing to give the bloke a hand.
UGH? UGH?
ER — I'M ALL RIGHT.
Suddenly—
HELP! I'VE BEEN ROBBED!
THAT'S BRISTLES BALDWIN! HE'S STOLEN ALL THE MONEY OUT OF MY TILL.
The strong arm of the law sprang into action! Charlie heaved a skittle after the crook.
AARGH!
WAHOO! YOU GOT HIM CHARLIE!
UM WOW!

Danny Blain came along just then to see what all the fuss was about. He was mighty pleased with his hairy chum!
WELL DONE, CHARLIE. LET'S GET THE VARMINT LOCKED UP!
PSST! SKITTLES GOOD, EH?
Soon, the shaken Bristles was tucked up safely in the jail.
THAT'S THAT! NOW LET'S GET BACK TO OUR SKITTLES.
UHUH!
WANTED
But—
HEY! THEY'VE GONE! SOMEBODY'S STOLEN THEM!
THIS IS A JOB FOR YOU, CHARLIE.
It didn't take long for Charlie to find some clues — the hoofprints of Indian ponies!
HERE'S THE FEATHER OUT OF A HEAD-DRESS!
GRR!

The big ape was angry. He'd been looking forward to a game of skittles and now the Indians had pinched them. He decided to follow the trail.
CHEERIO, CHARLIE. I HOPE YOU CATCH UP WITH THOSE THIEVING INDIANS SOON.
But the Indians had a big lead. Charlie trudged up and down hills for miles.
Then—
WAAH! BIG APE! ME MUST WARN REST OF TRIBE.
Soon after, the hairy sheriff came to the top of a hill overlooking an Indian camping site. Was this where he'd find the skittles? He hoped so!
UGH!

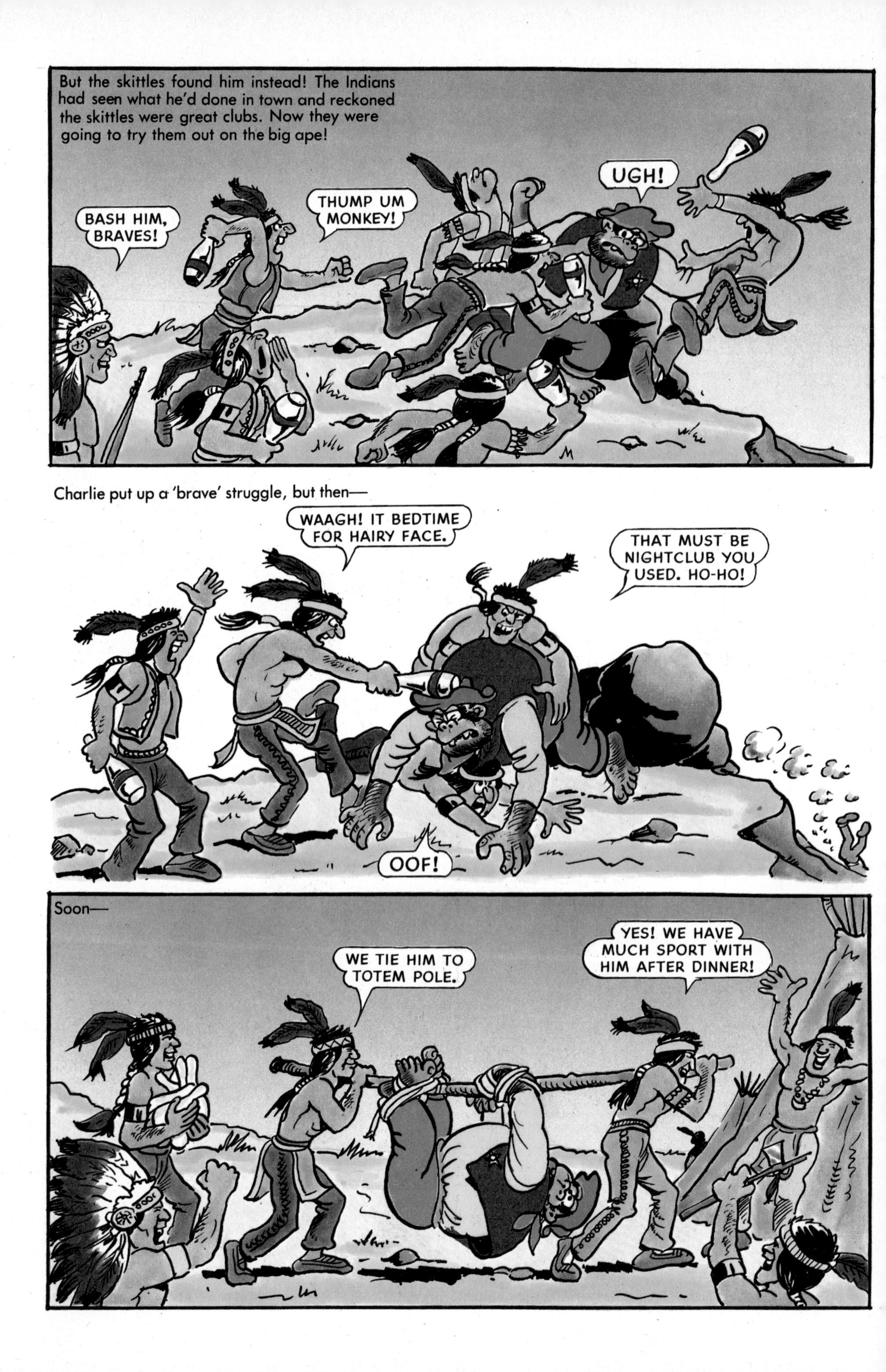
But the skittles found him instead! The Indians had seen what he'd done in town and reckoned the skittles were great clubs. Now they were going to try them out on the big ape!
BASH HIM, BRAVES!
THUMP UM MONKEY!
UGH!
Charlie put up a 'brave' struggle, but then—
WAAGH! IT BEDTIME FOR HAIRY FACE.
THAT MUST BE NIGHTCLUB YOU USED. HO-HO!
OOF!
Soon—
WE TIE HIM TO TOTEM POLE.
YES! WE HAVE MUCH SPORT WITH HIM AFTER DINNER!

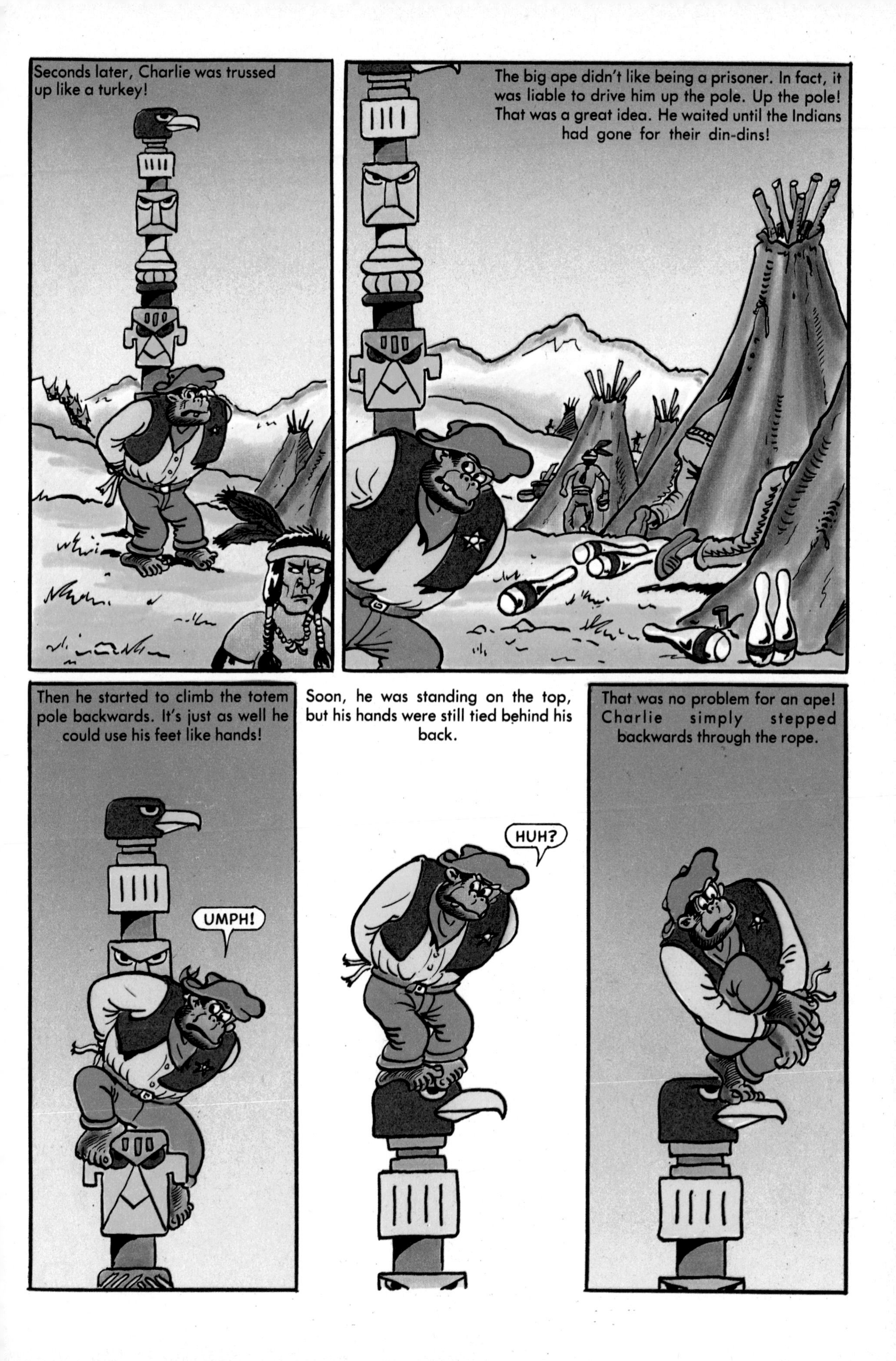
Seconds later, Charlie was trussed up like a turkey!
The big ape didn't like being a prisoner. In fact, it was liable to drive him up the pole. Up the pole! That was a great idea. He waited until the Indians had gone for their din-dins!
Then he started to climb the totem pole backwards. It's just as well he could use his feet like hands!
UMPH!
Soon, he was standing on the top, but his hands were still tied behind his back.
HUH?
That was no problem for an ape! Charlie simply stepped backwards through the rope.

But there wasn't much room for fancy footwork on the totem pole and, suddenly, he felt himself falling!
The fall didn't hurt Charlie — but the landing sure did!
OOYAH!
WHUMP!
The hairy sheriff's hands were still tied and he wasted no time in getting his teeth into his problem. But then—
WAAGH! APE IS TRYING TO ESCAPE!
OH-OH!
Charlie bent to pick up his young pals' skittles.

Next second, the Indians were upon him. But the big ape wasn't going to be captured so easily this time.
OW!
Charlie flattened the nearest Redskins and then he leapt on an Indian pony.
WUGH! WUGH!
WAAGH! MONKEY STEAL FASTEST HORSE. SHOOT UM!
WE NOT CATCH UM NOW.
ZING!
WHEE!
Hours later, the weary ape rode back into town.
WHEE! CHARLIE'S BACK —AND HE'S GOT OUR SKITTLES!

Chuck and Hank were keen to get on with a game of skittles, but some of them had been damaged in Charlie's escape!
OOGH!
HUH! THEY'VE GOT BULLET HOLES IN THEM.
SHERIFF'S OFFICE
Then the clever chimp had his second brainy idea of the week. He bored holes in the ends of the other skittles.
Soon, the three chums were playing again but, this time, the skittles were firmly fixed in place. Charlie had made sure no one else could pinch them.
GREAT SHOT, CHARLIE.
HUH-HUH!

A friendly Hilly? That's just silly!

DONG!
HERE GOES!
I'D BETTER WATCH WHAT HE'S UP TO!
WHACK!
OOPS! I'VE BROKEN THE AXE!
Then—
ZONK!
I'LL SAW DOWN THIS BIG TREE FOR THE BILLYS INSTEAD!
YEAH! GRANDPA HILLY TRIED TO KILL US!
LOOK AT THE BUMP HE GAVE ME!
LET'S GET OUR CLUBS AND BASH HIM!
Meanwhile—
I'LL ROLL THIS DOWN TO THE HUT AND SAW IT UP THERE!
LET'S GO.

Suddenly—
EEK!
OUCH!
OOH!
CRASH!
WHOOSH!
Soon after—
GRANDPA'S IN TROUBLE! GRAB YOUR GUNS, LADS!
HELP!
GRR!
BANG!
BANG!
BANG!
WE'RE GIVING THEM A PASTING THIS TIME! THANKS FOR BRINGING THEM STRAIGHT TO OUR SHACK, GRANDPA.

A big surprise when Mo gets the prize!

Later—
DING!
HM! MUGSY'S WON A COCONUT.
I'LL BET YOU COULDN'T DO THAT!
OH, YES, I COULD!
And—
I KNEW IT! YOU CAN'T EVEN LIFT THE MALLET!
I'LL GET A SMALLER MALLET.
And—
HO-HO! YOU WON'T GET A COCONUT WITH THAT!
OH, NO?
THUD!
OW!
THANK YOU!
HO-HO! WHO SAID I WOULDN'T GET A COCONUT?

Baby holds the key to saving a tree!
BABY CROCKETT
BAH! THIS TREE'S ALWAYS DROPPING LEAVES. I'M GOING TO CHOP IT DOWN.
WHAT?
KEEP BACK! YOU CAN'T CUT IT DOWN.
WHY NOT?
THE BIRDS WON'T HAVE ANYWHERE TO LIVE.
THE BIRDS HAVE ALL FLOWN SOUTH FOR THE WINTER.
HM!
WHAT ABOUT MY SWING?
THAT'S ALL THE MORE REASON FOR CUTTING DOWN THE TREE.
WELL, WHAT IF THE TREE FALLS ON THE GREENHOUSE?
I'D BETTER MEASURE HOW FAR AWAY IT IS.
So—
TEN METRES — ELEVEN . . .

THE TREE WON'T GET NEAR THE GREENHOUSE, BABY. BABY? WHERE ARE YOU?
ME'S LOCKED YOUR AXE IN THE SHED.
YOU LITTLE MONKEY!
GIVE ME THAT KEY.
NO!
Then—
GOT YOU!
OOPS!
Then—
AARGH!
Seconds later—
GRR!
ER—MAYBE WE SHOULD KEEP THE TREE AFTER ALL. AT LEAST WE'LL HAVE SOMEWHERE TO HIDE WHEN MUM'S ON THE WARPATH!

BEEZER

RIPAS
MOER
YEK NOWR
KOYOT
SCOWOM
DYENYS

1—Ginger is trying to read the airport timetable but the names of the foreign cities have been jumbled up. See if you can help him unscramble them.

2—Mo and Mirabelle think these 5 suitcases look the same but only 2 are, in fact, identical. Can you spot them?

1 2 3 4 5

3—The Badd Lads want to buy some fruit at the airport kiosk. Can you spot at least 8 objects beginning with the letter 'P'?

4—The Bunch have bought apples. Lanky has one less than Tiny and twice as many as Brainy, who has half as many as Thatch and one less than Dopey. If Dopey has 4 apples, how many do the rest have?

TEEZERS

5—The six Numskulls have gone missing while their man sleeps. See if you can find them.

6—There are 9 differences between these holiday posters. Blinky can't spot them. Can you?

7—The artist has made 10 deliberate mistakes in this picture of Pop pushing the trolley. Can you spot them?

ANSWERS

1 — Paris; Rome; New York; Tokyo; Moscow; Sydney.
2 — 1 and 4 are identical.
3 — Plates; Pipes; Pencils; Pictures; Plants; Pears; Postcards; Paper; are some of them.
4 — Lanky has 6; Brainy has 3; Tiny has 7 and Thatch has 6.
5 — Beside wrapping paper at kiosk; In bowl of apples at kiosk; Behind pipes at kiosk; In Brainy's bag of apples; Beside Dick on luggage trolley; Behind Blinky's brolly.
6 — Rope on front of yacht missing; Stripe on sail missing; Leaf on palm tree missing; Length of straw different; Highlight on glass missing; Newspaper layout different; Hatband missing; Pattern on shirt different; Stripes on deckchair different.
7 — Harry has 6 fingers; He has one long trouser leg; Dick has ear missing; He has different coloured socks; His 'Beezer' is spelled wrongly; Wheel on luggage trolley is missing; Pop has one short sleeve; He also has slipper on left foot; Suitcase has two handles; Harry's name on suitcase is spelled wrongly.

You're in for a treat when Sid's on the beat!

COME ON, SID — BUT KEEP QUIET. WE DON'T WANT TO SCARE HIM OFF. YOU'VE GOT TO USE YOUR HEAD, YOU KNOW!
Meanwhile—
PHEW! THIS IS HEAVY. I'LL DROP IT OUT OF THE WINDOW AND CLIMB DOWN THE DRAINPIPE!
Just then—
PHEW! I'M HOT WITH ALL THAT RUNNING!
And—
WOW! IT'S THAT COPPER AGAIN!
CLONK!
I'M OFF!
OOYAH! MY BONCE! WHAT HAPPENED?
YOU USED YOUR HEAD! HO-HO!
VERY FUNNY! HOP IT! I'LL USE MY TRUNCHEON ON THE CROOK THE NEXT TIME I SEE HIM!
Shortly—
I'LL GO FOR A WALK DOWN HERE AND KEEP OUT OF DAD'S WAY!

Then—
I WONDER IF FARMER GILES IS OUT!
COO! THERE'S THAT CROOK AGAIN!
HEH! I'VE GOT AN IDEA!
HERE'S A CARROT FOR YOU, DOBBIN!
Then—
ZONK!
POYNG!
And soon after—
HERE'S THE CROOK, DAD. I DIDN'T HAVE A TRUNCHEON, SO I USED A CARROT INSTEAD!

MY PAL Ropey
HELLO, folks. I'm Ron Rodgers and I've got an amazing piece of rope that once belonged to an Indian Fakir. My pal, Ropey, will do anything I ask him to — and that sometimes means trouble.
One morning, Mum sent me upstairs to waken Dad.
YOU'D BETTER GET UP, DAD, OR YOU'LL BE LATE FOR WORK.
I'M NOT GOING TO WORK. I DON'T FEEL WELL.
Mum wasn't exactly pleased when I told her the news.
OH, NO! YOU KNOW WHAT HE'S LIKE WHEN HE STAYS IN BED. HE'S A PERFECT PEST.
Soon after—
I'M OFF TO THE SHOPS. YOU CAN LOOK AFTER DAD.
THAT'S ALL RIGHT. ME AND ROPEY WILL MANAGE.
Shortly afterwards—
HOI! WILL SOMEONE BRING ME MY PIPE?
THUMP! THUMP!
Downstairs, I heard the racket.
THUMP!
THUMP!
HUH! I'M NOT RUNNING UPSTAIRS FOR HIM. YOU TAKE HIM A PIPE, ROPEY.

Now that was when things started to go wrong. I hadn't told my pal what kind of pipe Dad wanted. Ropey shot out of the window and headed for a trench that some water-board workers were digging.
Seconds later—
IS THAT YOU WITH THE PIPE? PUT IT DOWN OVER HERE.
That's exactly what Ropey did! Dad didn't half yell when the pipe was jammed over his head!
WAGH!
WHUMP!
Then—
RON! HELP ME TO GET THIS THING OFF.
OO-ER! YES, DAD.
What a struggle we had but at last—
THANK GOODNESS. I'M FREE. NOW I'M GOING BACK TO BED. YOU CAN BRING ME BREAKFAST.
ER — OKAY, DAD.

I soon rustled up a nice, tasty meal.
DAD WANTS BREAKFAST IN BED. TAKE IT TO HIM, ROPEY, AND NO MISTAKES THIS TIME!
But I'd told Ropey to give Dad breakfast in bed and—
SWOOSH!
AARGH!
YOU STUPID LUMP OF STRING! EVERYTHING'S SOAKING! YOU'D BETTER HANG ALL THE WET THINGS OUT TO DRY.
My pal streaked off with the soggy bedclothes and started to peg them on the rope.
Meanwhile, Dad was washing the egg out of his hair.

Suddenly—
HEY! WHAT'S HAPPENING?
Then—
EEK! ROPEY'S HANGING ME UP ON THE LINE, TOO.
I heard Dad shouting and almost fainted when I looked out of the window.
OH, NO! WHAT'S GOING TO HAPPEN NEXT?
I soon found out — and so did Dad!
RIP!
OOF!
Mum came home a few minutes later, just in time to see Dad storming out of the house.
DAD! I THOUGHT YOU WERE ILL.
SO I AM! BUT I'LL RECOVER MUCH FASTER AT WORK THAN I WILL IN THIS CRAZY HOUSE.

A big ho-ho in the snow!

Soon—
THAT'S FUNNY! THEIR TRACKS STOP AT THIS TREE!
Suddenly—
TURNIPS AWAY!
OOF!
LET'S GET THESE TURNIPS DOWN THE BURROW THEN RAID HIS STORE AGAIN.
But Farmer recovers, and—
I'LL GET YOU!
THEY WON'T GET AWAY! I CAN FOLLOW THEIR TRACKS!
Then—
AARGH!
NEE-HEE! HIDING THIS SIGN WAS A GOOD IDEA, PA!
DANGER THIN ICE

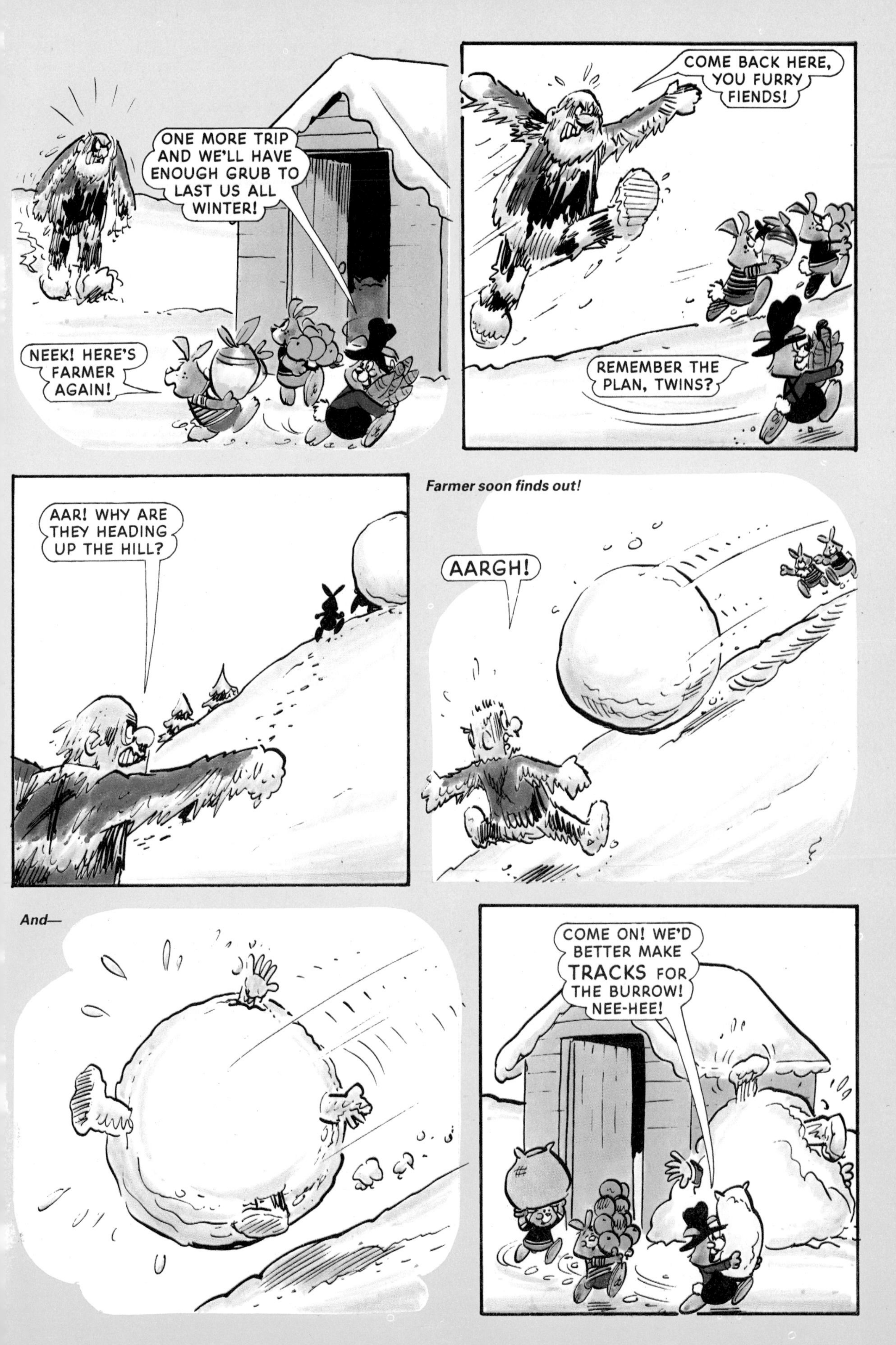
ONE MORE TRIP AND WE'LL HAVE ENOUGH GRUB TO LAST US ALL WINTER!
NEEK! HERE'S FARMER AGAIN!
COME BACK HERE, YOU FURRY FIENDS!
REMEMBER THE PLAN, TWINS?
AAR! WHY ARE THEY HEADING UP THE HILL?
Farmer soon finds out!
AARGH!
And—
COME ON! WE'D BETTER MAKE TRACKS FOR THE BURROW! NEE-HEE!

A shopping list is badly missed!

OOH! I'VE GOT SOMETHING IN MY EYE.
NOW LOOK WHAT YOU'VE DONE. HIS EYE'S WATERING.
I'LL THROW THE PLANE AWAY, BEFORE IT CAUSES ANY MORE DAMAGE.
At that moment—
NOW WHAT WAS IT AUNTIE ASKED ME TO GET? LET ME THINK.
WHERE DID THE LIST GO?
BRAIN DEPT
BYE, BYE, PLANE!
I CAN'T REMEMBER AT ALL. OH, DEAR!
HEY! LOOK WHAT FLEW IN. I'D BETTER TAKE IT TO OUR BRAIN DEPARTMENT.
MOUTH DEPT
And—
I'VE JUST REMEMBERED WHAT AUNTIE USUALLY GETS—POTATOES, CARROTS, SPAM, SOUP AND BISCUITS.
WHAT AN AMAZING MEMORY THAT MAN HAS. I WONDER HOW HE DOES IT.
ERAL STORE

The laughs are good when Hoss looks for food!

HUNGRY HOSS

OO-ER! I HOPE THOSE KIDS DON'T SCALP JOE!
Then—
UM ONE . . . UM TWO . . . UM THREE . . .
OH, NO!
OOYAH!
UM HUP!
OOH! I'LL BET THAT HURT!
I'D BETTER GET JOE DOWN.
OOH! AH!
Soon after—
LOSING A FIGHT AGAINST SOME KIDS WON'T MAKE JOE VERY FAMOUS.
I'LL TRY AGAIN.
OOYAH!

GRR! YOU BROKE UM BEST PEACE PIPE. YOU GET UM BLACK EYE!
ER . . . SORRY!
TAKE UM THAT!
GRR! THIS IS ALL YOUR FAULT, HOSS.
I'LL THUMP YOU!
I DON'T THINK HE'S TOO HAPPY!
Joe chases Hoss into town.
COME HERE, YOU STUPID HOSS!
Suddenly—
BULLY A POOR, OLD HORSE, EH? TAKE THAT!
JOE'S STILL NOT FAMOUS, BUT I'M GETTING GOODIES NOW! YUM! MUNCH!
POOR HORSEY! HAVE A LUMP OF SUGAR. DID THE NASTY MAN SCARE YOU, THEN?

JOE SOAP
JOE BROWN was known as Joe Soap by the people in Sudbury. You see, he was always blowing amazing bubbles made by his grandfather, a real crackpot inventor.
One day—
LOOK, JOE! I'VE MADE A NEW BUBBLE MIXTURE.
GREAT, GRANDAD.
I'LL TRY IT OUT ON MY SNOWMAN FIRST.
But there's a sudden gust of wind and—
WHOOSH!
SPLUT!
OOPS! SORRY, GRANDPA!
Suddenly—
FLASH!
EEK! YOU'VE TURNED INTO A DRAGON! SPEAK TO ME.

Grandad is blazing mad and when he opens his mouth—
AAIIEE! FLAMES!
YOU SET FIRE TO MY SHED! YOU WON'T GET ANY POCKET MONEY UNTIL I GET A NEW ONE.
AW, DAD! IT WAS AN ACCIDENT!
I'VE ONLY GOT FIFTY PENCE. THAT WON'T LAST VERY LONG.
WRESTLI
BIG HAYSTACK V GIANT DADDY
Just then—
GREENGROCER'S
HEY! WE COULD ROAST CHESTNUTS AND SELL THEM TO SKATERS ON THE POND. WE'LL MAKE A FORTUNE!
CHESTNUTS —50p PER KILO!

Soon—
THAT'S IT, GRANDAD! YOU ROAST THE NUTS AND I'LL SELL THEM.
But Grandad's hot breath starts to melt the ice.
EEK! THE ICE IS CRACKING!
KRAAK
SPLOOSH
YAROO!
HELP!
EEK!
MU-UM!
AARGH!
GROOH!
OO-ER! LOOK WHAT YOU'VE DONE, GRANDAD!
GRR! THAT WAS YOUR FAULT.
IT'S TIME WE WEREN'T HERE, GRANDAD.
MENACES!
GRR!

COME BACK AND GET BELTED!
GASP! THEY'RE GOING TO CATCH US.
WHAT ABOUT TRYING TO FLY?
So—
COME ON, GRANDAD. GET YOUR FEET OFF THE GROUND.
PUFF! PANT! I'M TRYING.
FLAP
FLAP
Then—
WHEE! WE HAVE LIFT-OFF!
ZOOM
Soon—
WE'RE WELL AWAY NOW.
THANK GOODNESS! MY WINGS ARE ACHING! I'LL HAVE TO LAND.

ER — AREN'T YOU COMING DOWN TOO FAST, GRANDAD?
I DON'T KNOW! I'VE NEVER DONE THIS BEFORE.
BUMP! THUMP! CRASH!
OOH! WELL, WE GOT DOWN IN ONE PIECE — JUST!
Suddenly—
WE SAW WHAT YOU DID AT THE POND. NOW YOU CAN HELP US.
EH? WHAT'S GOING ON?
COME HERE, YOU.
HOI! STOP "DRAGON" ME BY THE TAIL.

WE RAN OUT OF GAS FOR OUR HOT-AIR BALLOON. BUT YOUR DRAGON WILL DO JUST AS WELL.
SWAG
YEAH! START BLOWING INTO THE BALLOON OR ELSE . . .
Seconds later—
WHEE! WE GOT AWAY JUST IN TIME.
HUFF! PUFF!
VROOM!
POLICE
BAH! THOSE BANK RAIDERS HAVE ESCAPED AGAIN.
HO-HO! THE COPS WON'T CATCH US NOW.
SCREECH!
Suddenly, the effect of the bubbles wears off! Grandad returns to normal!
HOI! WHAT HAPPENED?
SWAG

Then—
WE'RE GOING DOWN.
WE MUST LOSE WEIGHT!
CHUCK EVERYTHING OVER THE SIDE.
EVERYTHING?
THERE! THAT'S GOT RID OF THAT HEAVY BAG.
EEK! OUR LOOT!
SWAG
Down below—
WHUMP!
SWAG
WOW! THEY'VE DROPPED THE MONEY FROM THE BANK RAID.
POLICE
OSS 230

Meanwhile—
GRR! WE'VE GOT A GOOD MIND TO THROW YOU TWO OVERBOARD.
But then—
WOW! WE'VE HIT A TREE.
CRASH
AAGH!
AAIIEE!
OKAY, MEN! TAKE THOSE CROOKS AWAY.
CLICK
Then—
WELL DONE, YOU TWO. THERE WILL BE A BIG REWARD FOR THIS.
ER — THAT'S NICE.
Later—
THE REWARD PAID FOR A NEW SHED FOR DAD — AND WE'VE GOT PLENTY LEFT. WHAT WOULD YOU LIKE, GRANDAD?
OOH! JUST A PACKET OF LOZENGES. MY THROAT FEELS AS IF IT'S ON FIRE.

You'll have a tee-hee at the twins' house in a tree!

WE'LL HAVE TO STOCK OUR HOUSE WITH GRUB BUT I DON'T FANCY RUNNING BACKWARDS AND FORWARDS TO THE LARDER.
OOH! AH!
DON'T WORRY. I'VE GOT AN IDEA.
And soon —
HERE COMES THE BUCKET!
OKAY! I'M READY!
Meanwhile —
THAT WAS A NICE SNACK.
Then —
OOF!
OOPS! I MISSED THE BUCKET.
GRR! YOU'D BETTER CLEAN THAT UP, YOU PEST. I'M GOING BACK OUTSIDE FOR A SNOOZE.
OKAY, POP.
After Dick has cleared up —
RIGHT, HARRY! THE BUCKET'S FULL OF GRUB. HAUL AWAY!

HEE-HEE! THIS IS A GREAT IDEA OF DICK'S.
Suddenly —
SNAP!
And —
CLANG!
OUCH!
GRR! THAT WAS YOUR FAULT.
OO-ER!
COME HERE AND BE THUMPED!
NOT LIKELY!
I'LL NIP UP HERE.
Then —
HEY! WHAT'S POP DOING?
HELP! WE CAN'T GET DOWN WITHOUT THE LADDER!
HEE-HEE! I KNOW! NOW I'LL GET SOME PEACE!

Why does Baby C get as mucky as can be?

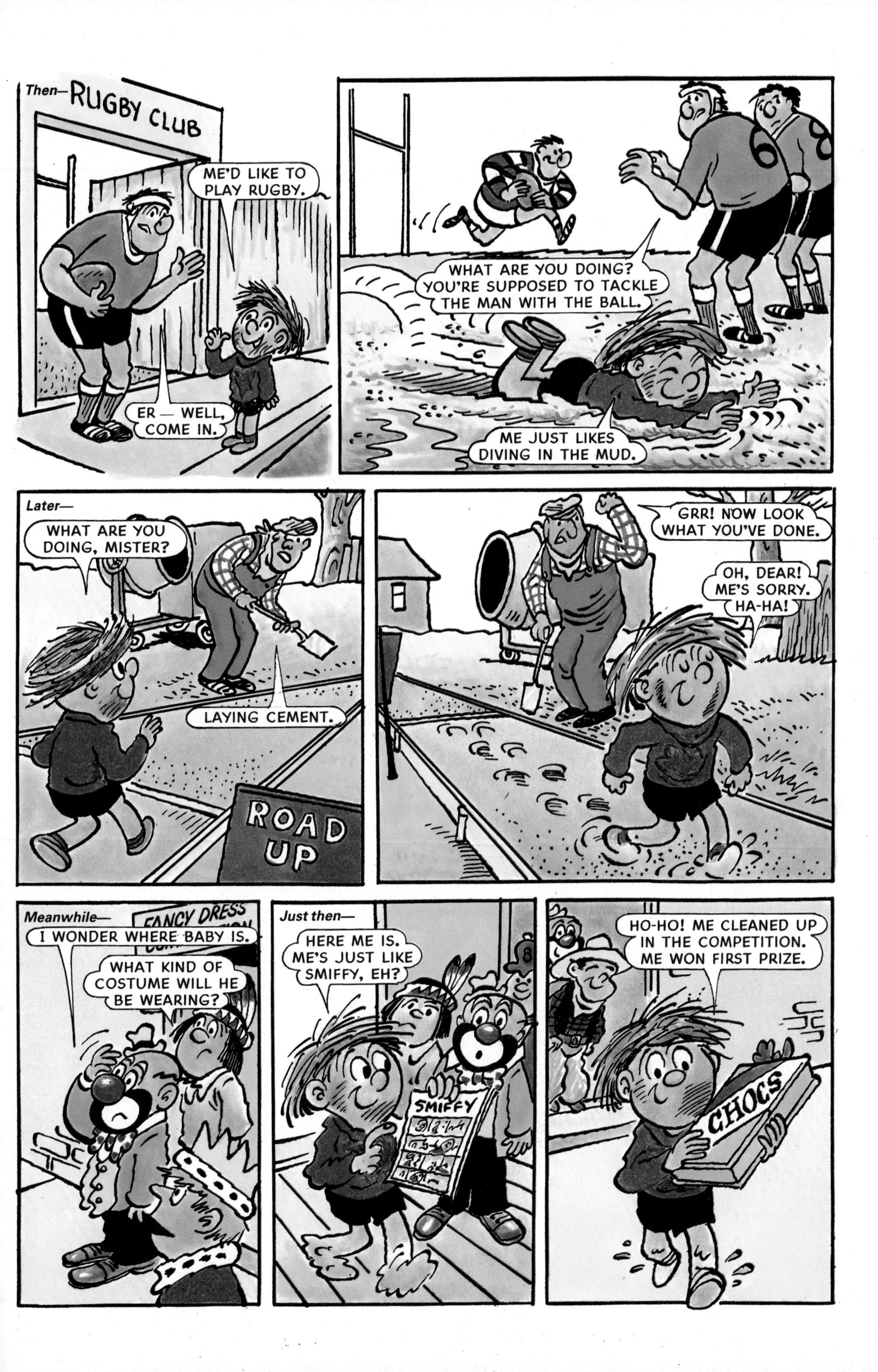
Then—
RUGBY CLUB
ME'D LIKE TO PLAY RUGBY.
ER — WELL, COME IN.
WHAT ARE YOU DOING? YOU'RE SUPPOSED TO TACKLE THE MAN WITH THE BALL.
ME JUST LIKES DIVING IN THE MUD.
Later—
WHAT ARE YOU DOING, MISTER?
LAYING CEMENT.
ROAD UP
GRR! NOW LOOK WHAT YOU'VE DONE.
OH, DEAR! ME'S SORRY. HA-HA!
Meanwhile—
FANCY DRESS
I WONDER WHERE BABY IS.
WHAT KIND OF COSTUME WILL HE BE WEARING?
Just then—
HERE ME IS. ME'S JUST LIKE SMIFFY, EH?
SMIFFY
HO-HO! ME CLEANED UP IN THE COMPETITION. ME WON FIRST PRIZE.
CHOCS

There are easier ways to get out of a maze!

But—
OOPS! I DIDN'T VAULT HIGH ENOUGH!
I'LL DO IT THIS TIME.
But—
ERK! SORRY! I DIDN'T SEE YOU!
OW!
GRR! WAIT TILL I CATCH YOU!
I'D BETTER GET OUT OF HERE!
And—
PLUG'S TAKING HIS TIME.
I'VE DONE IT!
TRAMPOLINES
10p per 5min.
LET'S GO IN AND SEE HOW HE'S GETTING ON.
EEK!
BOYNG!
AMPOLINES
10p PER 5min.
HO-HO! I DON'T KNOW HOW HE GOT INTO THAT POSITION. IT'S "A-MAZE-ING"!

The Billys all dread Hunk using his head!

So—
OOF!
OO-ER! I'D BETTER TAKE COVER!
But—
CRASH!
OOF!
AAROOGH!
WHAT'S HAPPENING?
EEK!
CRASH!
OW!
Then—
HE'S STUCK! BRING SOME ROPES.
And—
RIGHT! TIE HIM TO THIS CART!

Meanwhile—
HEE-HEE! I BET HUNK'S GIVING THEM BILLYS A HARD TIME!
Suddenly—
THERE HE GOES!
OH-OH! INTO THE SHACK, LADS.
THERE! WE'LL BE SAFE NOW!
That's what they think!
CRASH!
HELP!
AAGH!
OW!
CRASH!
YOW!
AAIIEEE!
OOYAH!
THUD!
HO-HO! THAT'S WHAT I CALL USING THE HEAD!

Things look bad for this scruffy lad!

I'LL PATCH IT UP ONCE I'VE GOT THE PICTURE IN PLACE.
But when Smiffy tries again to hammer the nail into the wall—
CRASH!
AARGH! THE MIRROR!
MUM'LL BE FURIOUS IF SHE SEES THE DAMAGE I'VE CAUSED.
I'D BETTER START REPAIRING THINGS. I'LL START WITH THE WALL.
PLASTER
HMM! I'M NOT VERY GOOD AT PLASTERING. I'M MAKING A RIGHT MESS.
I'LL COVER IT UP WITH A STRIP OF WALLPAPER.

But—
OO-ER! THIS BOX IS GIVING WAY!
CREAK!
I'LL JUMP ON TO THE RADIATOR.
OH, NO!
CREAK!
IT'S FALLING!
AAAARGH!
RIP!
Just then—
SMIFFY! WHAT ON EARTH HAVE YOU BEEN DOING?
ER . . . I WAS TIDYING MY BEDROOM, MUM . . .